Stories of Santa

Up on the Housetop
Jolly Old St. Nicholas

A STORYBOOK OF TWO BELOVED SANTA SONGS

Hallmark

STORIES OF SANTA

Copyright © 2003
Hallmark Licensing, Inc.

Artwork from the Masterworks Collection
HALLMARK ARCHIVES AND DESIGN COLLECTION

Published by Hallmark Cards, Inc.
Kansas City, Missouri 64141

Visit us on the Web at www.Hallmark.com.

All rights reserved. No portion of this publication may
be reproduced, stored in a retrieval system, or transmitted in any
form by any means — electronic, mechanical, photographic, recorded,
or any other — except for brief quotations in printed reviews,
without the prior written permission of the publisher.

Printed and bound in Brazil.

to

from

Up on the Housetop

BENJAMIN R. HANBY

1. Up on the house-top rein-deer pause, Out jumps good old Santa Claus;
2. First comes the stock-ing of lit-tle Nell, Oh, dear San-ta fill it well;
3. Next comes the stock-ing of lit-tle Will, Oh, just see what a glo-rious fill;

Down through the chim-ney with lots of toys, All for the lit-tle ones' Christ-mas joys!
Give her a dol-ly that laughs and cries, One that will o-pen and shut her eyes!
Here is a ham-mer and lots of tacks, Al-so a ball and whip that cracks.

Ho! Ho! Ho! Who would-n't go? Ho! Ho! Ho! Who would-n't go? Up on the house-top;
Ho! Ho! Ho! Who would-n't go? Ho! Ho! Ho! Who would-n't go? Up on the house-top;
Ho! Ho! Ho! Who would-n't go? Ho! Ho! Ho! Who would-n't go? Up on the house-top;

Click! Click! Click! Down through the chim-ney with good Saint Nick!
Click! Click! Click! Down through the chim-ney with good Saint Nick!
Click! Click! Click! Down through the chim-ney with good Saint Nick!

UP ON THE HOUSETOP

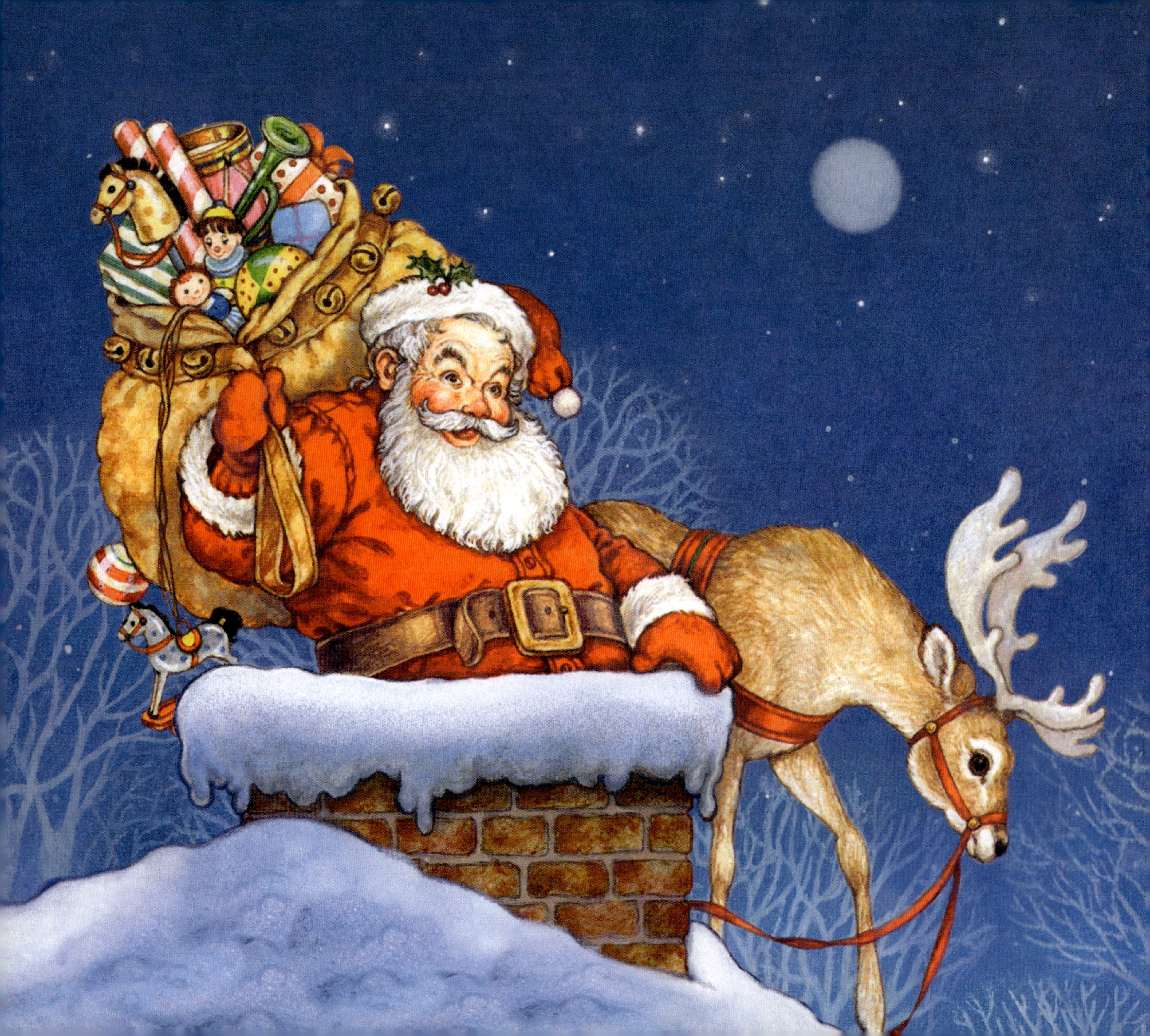

Up on the housetop reindeer pause,
Out jumps good old Santa Claus,
Down through the chimney with lots of toys,
All for the little ones' Christmas joys!

First comes the stocking of little Nell,
Oh, dear Santa, fill it well...

Give her a dolly that laughs and cries,
One that will open and shut her eyes!

Next comes the stocking of little Will,
Oh, just see what a glorious fill…

Here is a hammer and lots of tacks,
Also a ball...and a whip that cracks.

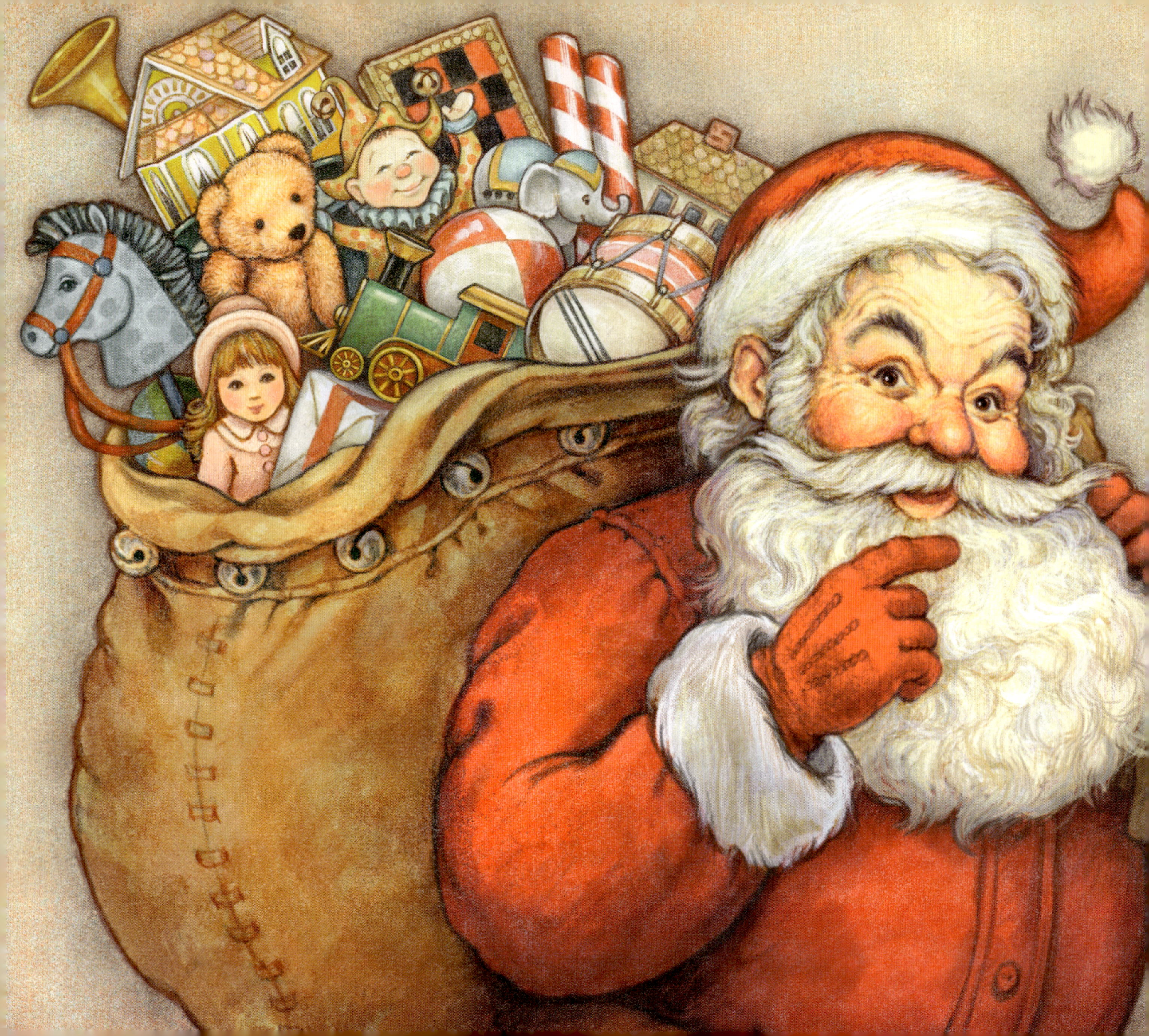

Ho! Ho! Ho!
Who wouldn't go?
Ho! Ho! Ho!
Who wouldn't go?

Up on the housetop...
Click! Click! Click!
Down through the chimney
with good Saint Nick.

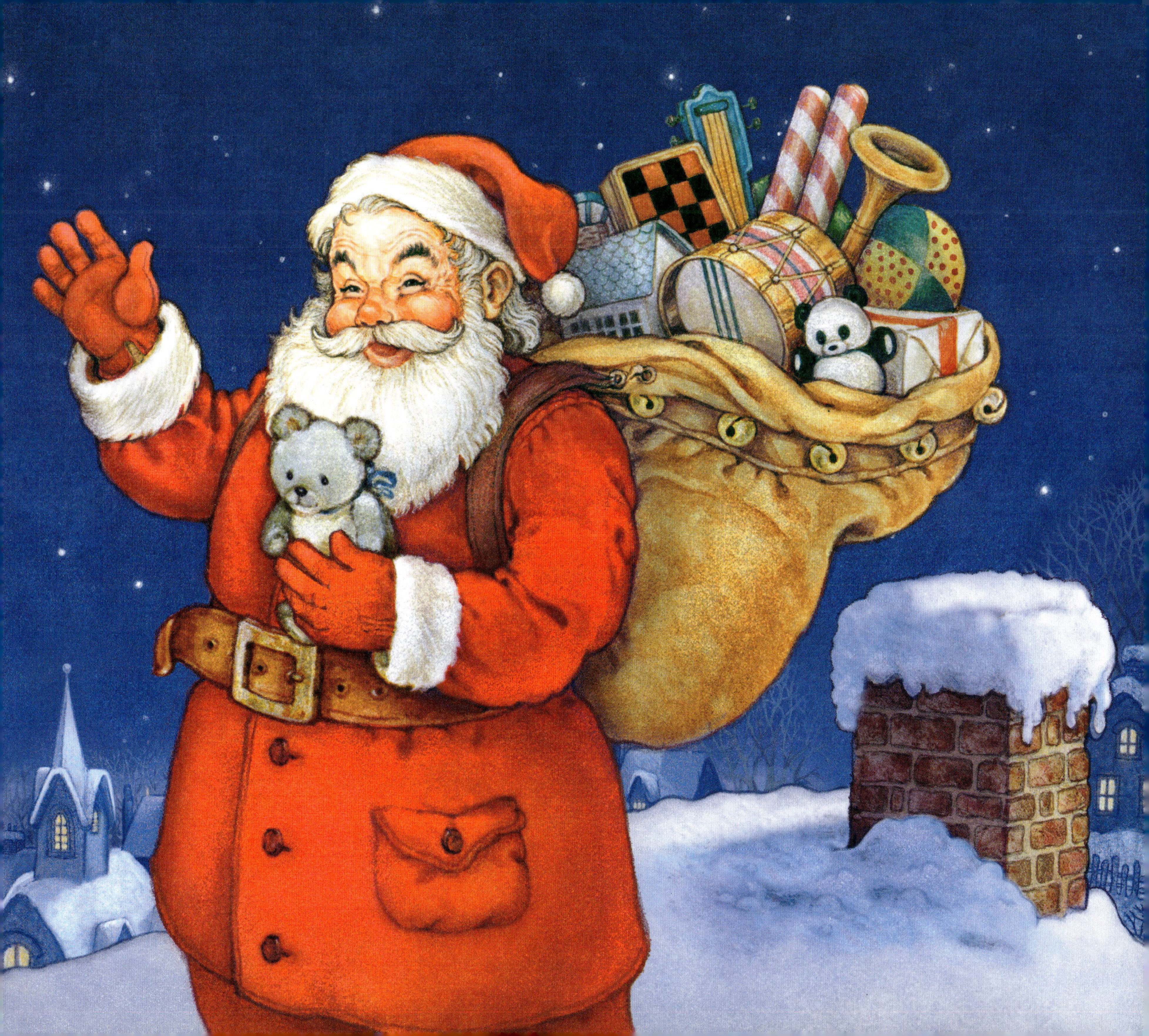

Favorite gifts from Santa

Christmas songs and stories we love

The best part of Christmas

SANTA AND ME

FAMILY PHOTOS

All I want for Christmas

Our best Christmas memories

Jolly Old Saint Nicholas

1. Jol - ly old Saint Ni - cho - las, Lean your ear this way!
2. When the clock is strik - ing twelve, When I'm fast a - sleep,
3. John - ny wants a pair of skates, Su - sy wants a sled.

Don't you tell a sin - gle soul What I'm going to say;
Down the chim - ney broad and black, With your pack you'll creep;
Nel - lie wants a pict - ure book, Yel - low, blue, and red.

Christ - mas Eve is com - ing soon; Now, my dear old man,
All the stock - ings you will find Hang - ing in a row;
Now I think I'll leave to you What to give the rest.

Whis - per what you'll bring to me; Tell me if you can.
Mine will be the short - est one, You'll be sure to know.
Choose for me, dear San - ta Claus, You will know the best.

Jolly Old Saint Nicholas

Jolly old Saint Nicholas,
Lean your ear this way!
Don't you tell a single soul
What I'm going to say.

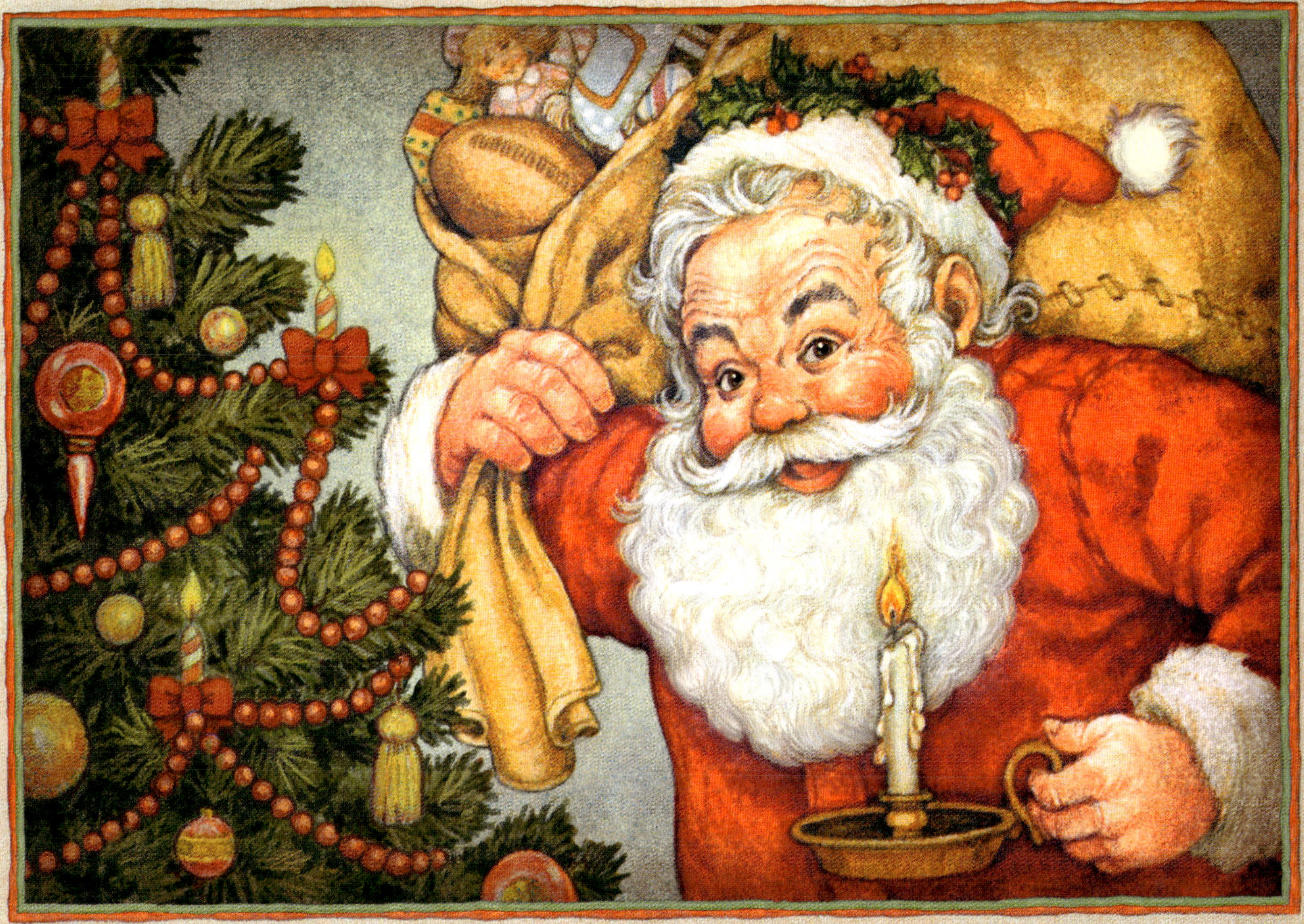

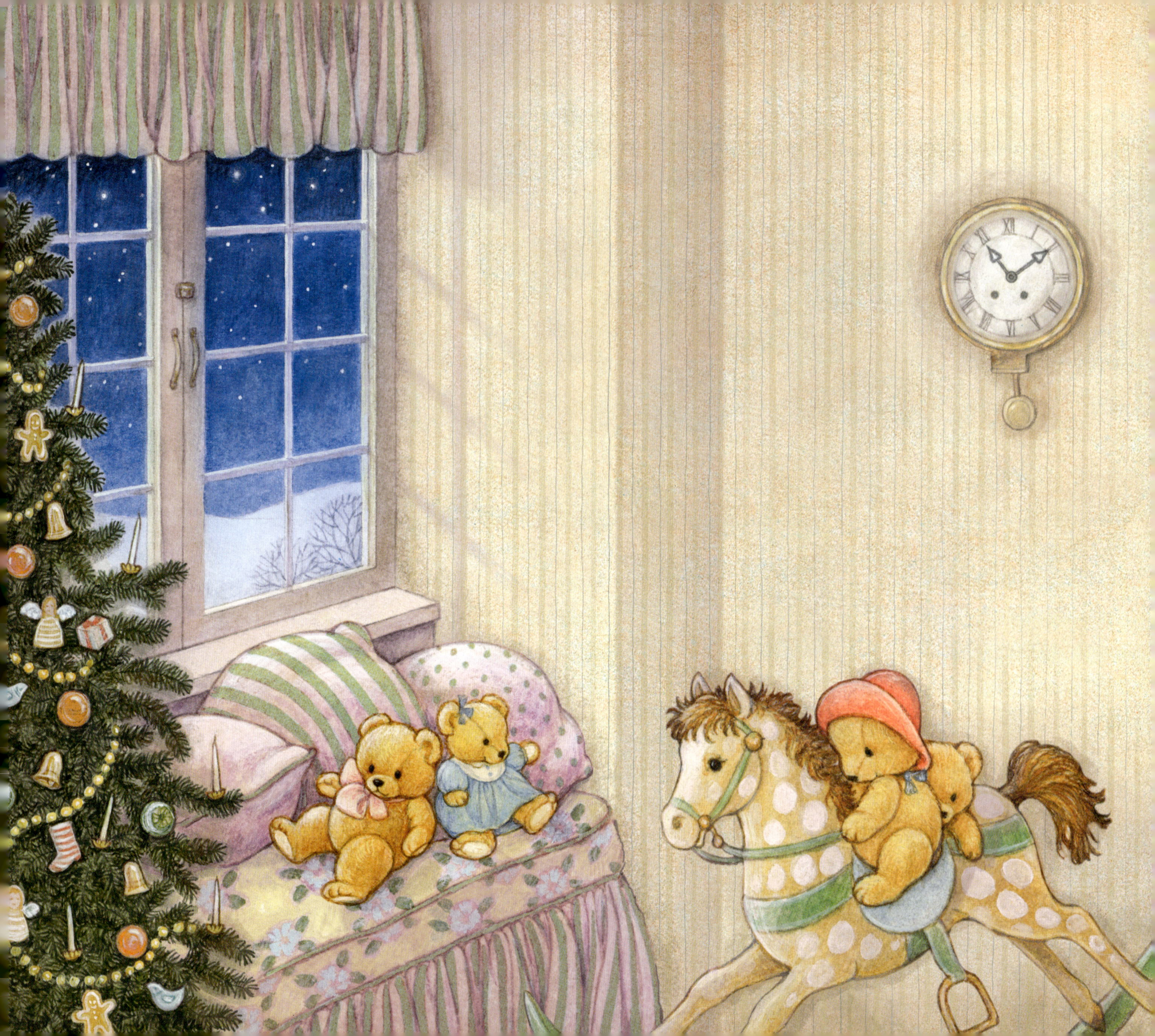

Christmas Eve is coming soon.
Now, my dear old man,
Whisper what you'll bring to me,
Tell me, if you can.

When the clock is striking twelve,
When I'm fast asleep,
Down the chimney, broad and black,
With your pack you'll creep.

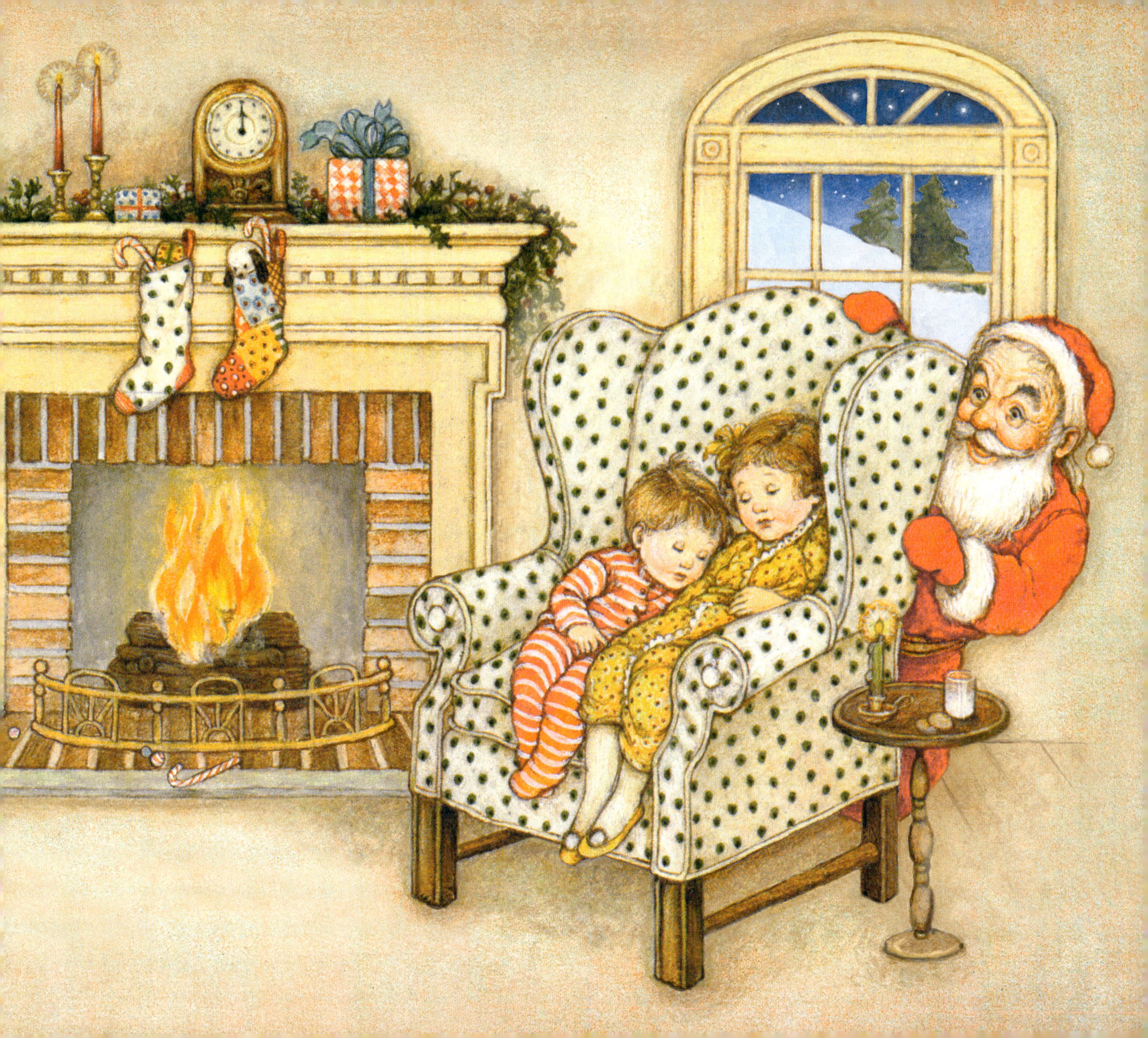

All the stockings you will find
Hanging in a row.
Mine will be the shortest one,
You'll be sure to know.

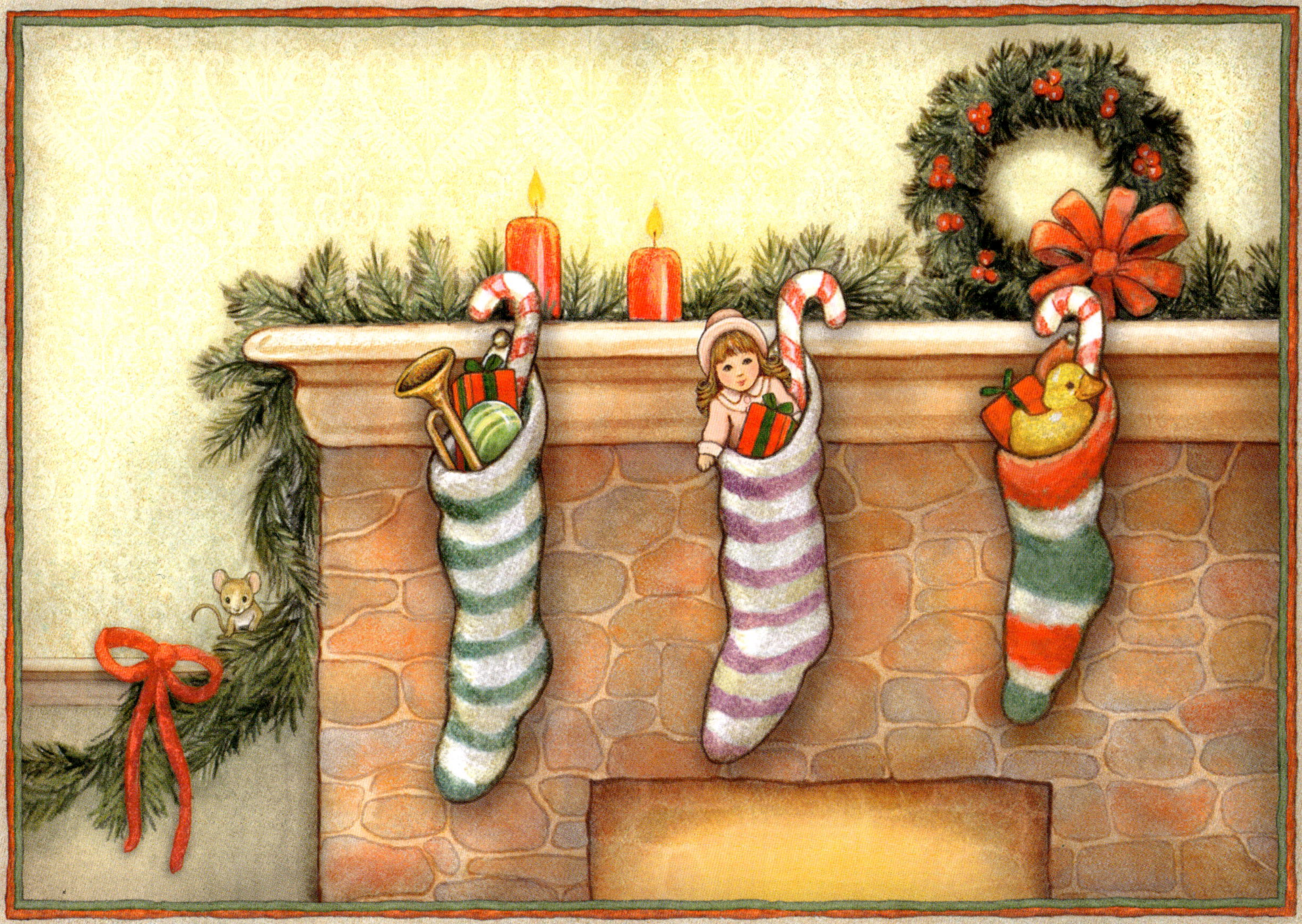

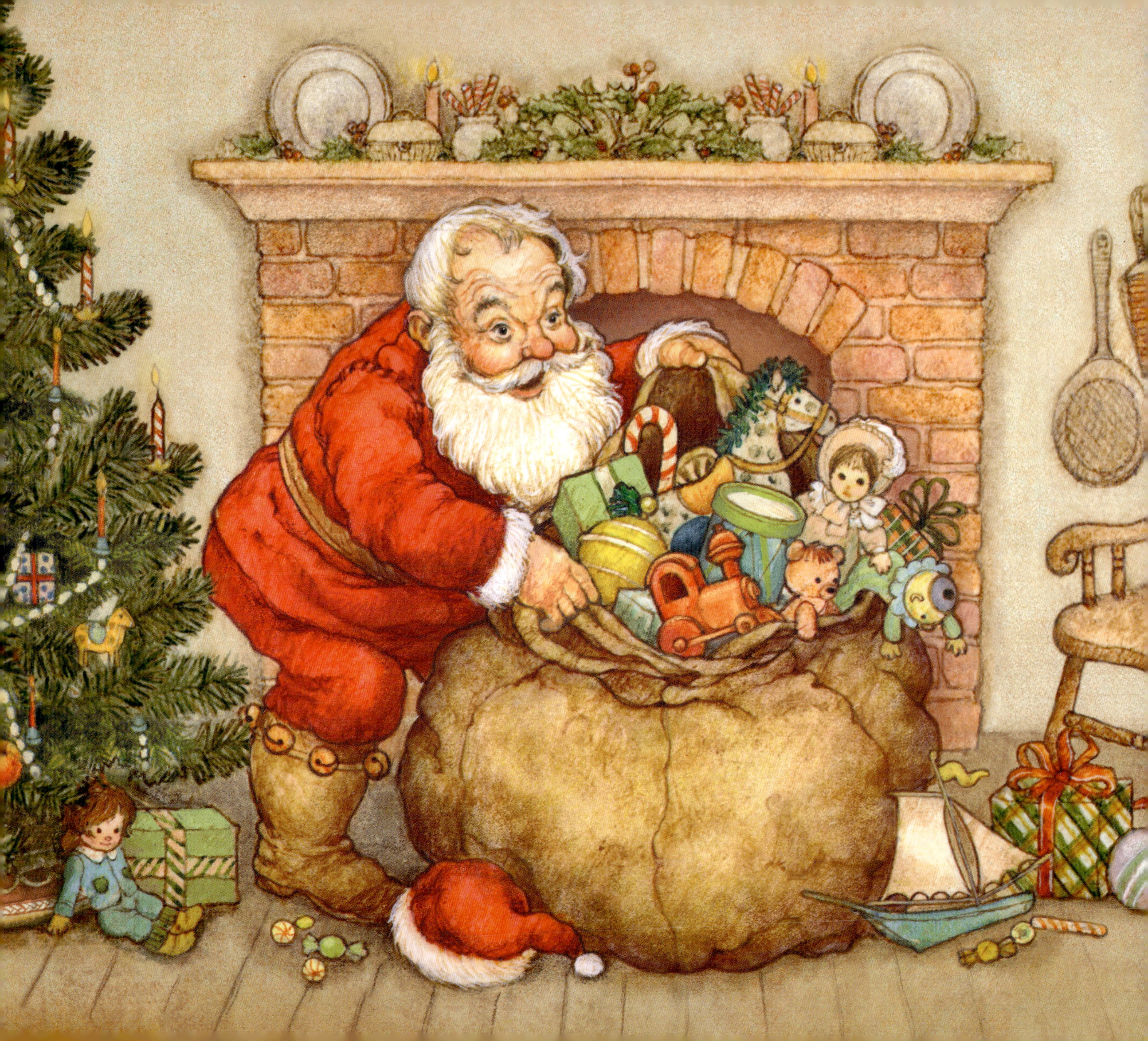

Johnny wants a pair of skates.
Susy wants a sled.
Nellie wants a picture book,
Yellow, blue, and red.

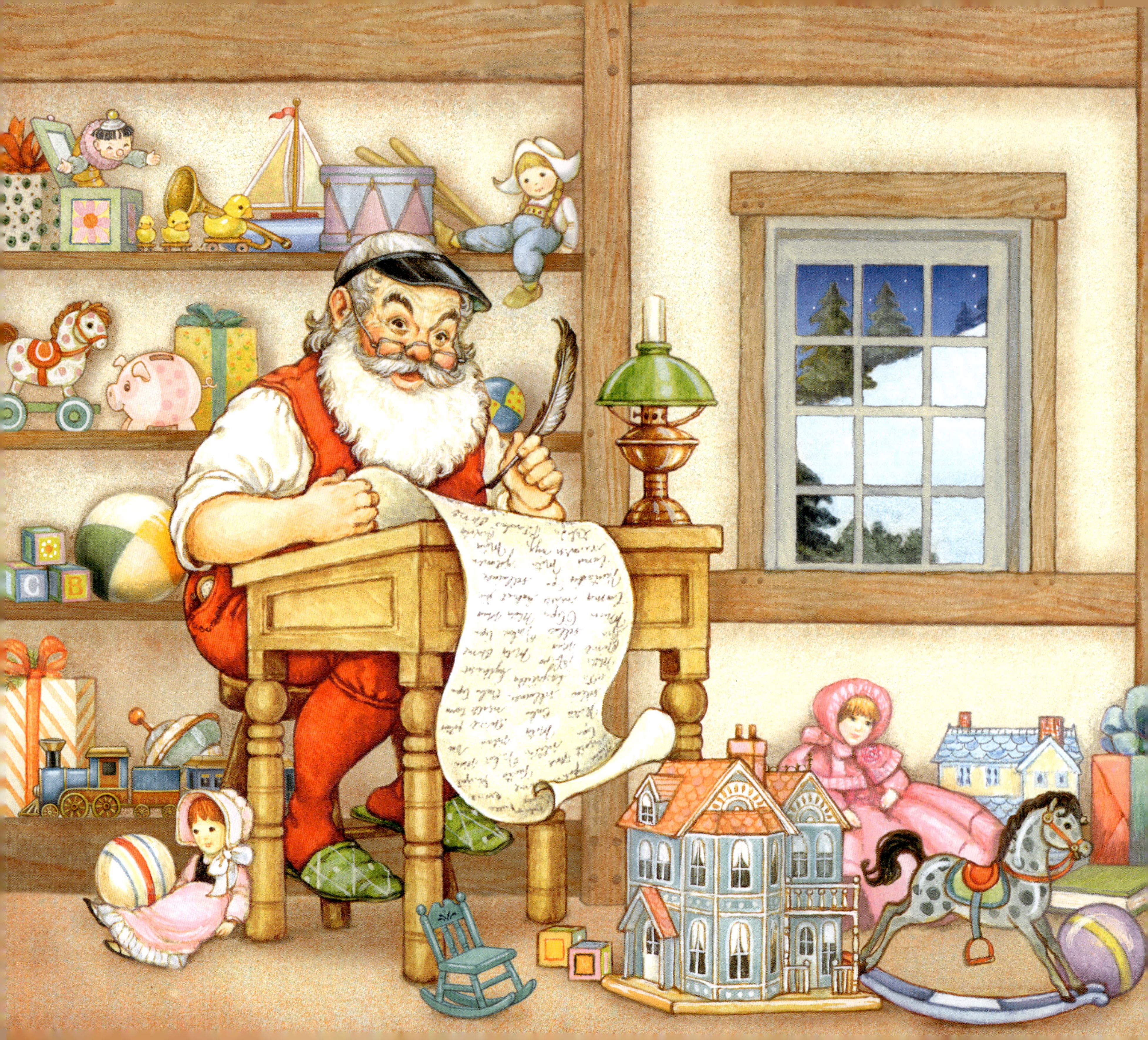

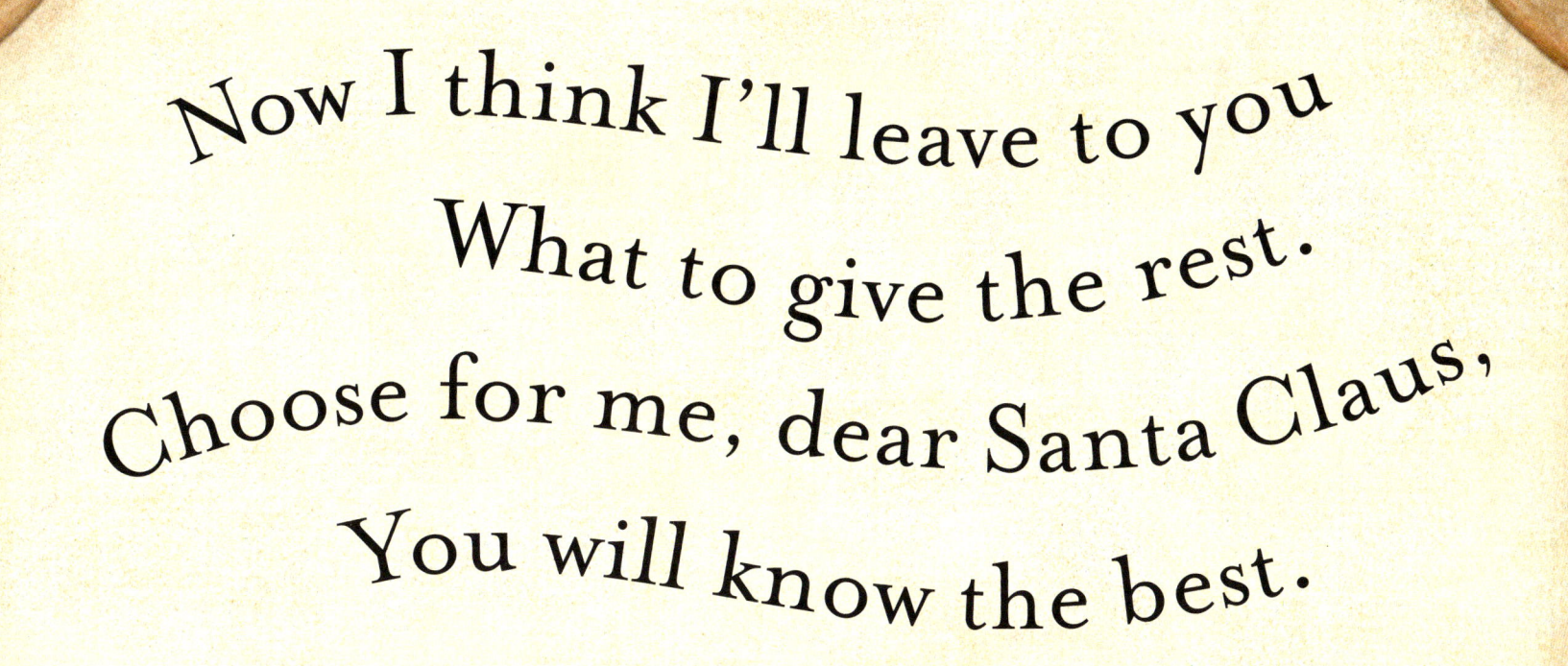

Now I think I'll leave to you
What to give the rest.
Choose for me, dear Santa Claus,
You will know the best.

Benjamin Russell Hanby

JULY 22, 1833 — MARCH 16, 1867

BENJAMIN HANBY was many things in his short lifetime — a student, an abolitionist, a father, and a teacher. But he is most remembered as a composer. And even though he wrote more than 70 songs and hymns, including the Civil War song *Darling Nelly Gray*, the one he's most known for is *Up on the Housetop*. Some believe it was the first American song of any importance about Santa Claus, and it is one of the first secular Christmas songs composed in the United States. The exact date of its writing isn't known, but it is thought to have been created in the 1860s. While there isn't evidence to prove it, some historians believe that Hanby also might have composed *Jolly Old Saint Nicholas,* which dates back to about the same time period and has similar musical styling and lyrics.